The Swiss Family Robinson

Simplified

Based on *The Swiss Family Robinson*
by Johann Wyss

A Beka Book® Pensacola, FL 32523-9100
an affiliate of PENSACOLA CHRISTIAN COLLEGE®

Introduction

Children are eagerly searching for a workable sense of values. They need reading material that will give them ideals to reach for and examples to follow.

The Swiss Family Robinson is a classic story that has entertained readers for many years. When the family find themselves stranded on a desert island after a shipwreck, they learn to use the island's natural resources to make a comfortable home. Many character values, including creativity, resourcefulness, and faith in God, are woven throughout the book.

The Swiss Family Robinson (simplified)

Based on *The Swiss Family Robinson* by Johann Wyss

Staff Credits

Cover Design: Stan Shimmin
Designer: Michelle Johnson
Illustrators: Steven Hileman, Dan Cordova, John Ball, Christy Hudson

Cataloging Data
Wyss, Johann David, 1743–1818.
    The Swiss family Robinson: simplified / based
on the Swiss family Robinson by Johann Wyss;
editor, Heidi Mayfield.
    vi, 130 p.; ill.; 19 cm.
    1. Family life—Juvenile fiction. 2. Survival after
airplane accidents, shipwrecks, etc.—Fiction.
III. Mayfield, Heidi. IV. A Beka Book, Inc.
Library of Congress: PZ7 .W996 Swi 2000
Dewey System: Fic Wys

Table of Contents

Chapter

1 Shipwrecked and Alone...........1

2 We Explore the Island............15

3 The Tree House........................25

4 A Day of Rest...........................35

5 Useful Discoveries...................41

6 The Rainy Season.....................57

7 The Salt Cavern.......................66

8 The Farm.................................74

9 Bears and Ostriches...............83

10 Jenny.....................................100

11 New Switzerland...................117

Robinson Family Album

Mr. Robinson

Mrs. Robinson

Fritz
(16 Years Old)

Ernest
(13 Years Old)

Jack
(10 Years Old)

Franz
(8 Years Old)

Chapter 1
Shipwrecked and Alone

When one has a good tale to tell, he should try to be brief, and not say more than he can help; so I shall not say a word of what took place on board the ship till we had been six days in a storm. The ship had gone far out of her true course, and no one on board knew where we were. The masts lay in splints on the deck, a leak in the side of the ship let more in than the crew could pump out, and each one felt that before long he would find a grave in the deep sea, which sent its spray from side to side of what was now but a mere hulk.[1]

"Come, boys," I said to my four sons, who were with me, "God can save us if it please Him

---

[1]hulk—*a wrecked ship that is unfit for sailing*

to do so; but, if this is to be our last hour, let us bow to His will—we shall at least go down side by side."

My dear wife could not hide the tears that fell down her cheeks as I thus spoke to my sons, but she was calm, and knelt down to pray, while the boys clung round her as if they thought she could help them.

Just then we heard a cry of "Land! land!" We felt a shock, and it was clear that we had struck a rock, for we heard a loud cry from one of the men, "We are lost! Launch the boat; save yourselves!"

I went at once on deck, and found that all the boats had been let down, and that the last of the crew had just left the ship. I cried out for the men to come back and take us with them, but it was in vain.

I then thought that our last chance was gone. Still, as I felt the ship was not sinking, I went to the stern,[2] and found, to my joy, that she was held up by a piece of rock on each side, and stuck fast like a wedge. At the

---

[2]stern—*the rear section of a ship or boat*

same time I saw some trace of land, which lay to the south, and this made me return to my family with some hope that we had still a faint chance.

As soon as I got downstairs I took my wife by the hand and said, "Be of good cheer, we are at least safe for some time, and if the wind should change, we may yet reach the land that lies but a short way off."

I said this to calm the fears of my wife and sons, and it did so far more than I had a right to hope.

"Let us eat some food," said my wife. "We are sure to need it, for this will no doubt be a night to try our strength."

My wife got some food for the boys, which we were glad to see them eat, poor as it was; but we could not share their meal. Three out of the four were put to bed, and soon went to sleep; but Fritz, who was our first child, would not leave us. He said, like a good son, that he would try to be of some use, and think what could be done.

"If we could but find some cork," Fritz said to me in a low tone, "we might make floats. You and I will not need them, for we can swim, but the rest will need some such means to keep them up."

"A good thought," I said. "Let us try to find what things there are in the ship that we can make use of."

We soon found some casks[3] and ropes, and with these we made a kind of float for each of the three boys, and then my wife made one for her own use. This done, we got some knives,

---

[3]cask—*a barrel*

string, and such things that we could secure to our belts. We did not fail to look for and find a flint[4] and steel, and the box in which the burnt rags were kept, for these were at that time the means of lighting a fire.

Fritz, who was now well-nigh worn out, lay down on his bed and slept like the rest. As for me and my poor wife, we kept watch, each in fear lest the next wave should lift the ship off the rock and break it up.

I need not tell you how glad we were when we saw the first gleam of light. At dawn the wind did not blow so strongly, the sky was clear of clouds, and we saw the sun rise, and with it rose our hopes. I soon had my wife and sons on deck.

"Where are the men?" they said. "How can we steer the ship?"

"My dear boys," I said, "He who has kept us safe till now will still aid us. Let all hands set to work, and leave the rest to God."

At these words we all went to work with a will. My wife went to feed the livestock; Fritz

---

[4]flint—*a piece of rock that sparks when struck with steel*

set off in search of weapons; and Ernest made his way to the tool chest. Jack ran to pick up what he could find, but as he got to one of the doors he gave it a push, and two huge dogs sprang out and leaped at him. He thought at first that they would bite him, but he soon found that they meant him no harm, and one of them let him get on his back and ride up to me as I came from the bottom of the ship.

When the boys had done their search, and the spoil was brought on deck, we thought we had found all that we should need. "As for me," said my wife, "I have brought good news, for we still have on board a cow, a donkey, two goats, six sheep, a ram, a pig, and a sow, and I have found food for them all."

"All that you bring will be of use," I said; "but I fear that Jack's dogs will do us more harm than good."

"Not at all," said Jack, "for they can help us to hunt when we get to land."

"Well said, Jack. And now let us see what we can do that will aid us to get there."

We then took the casks that we had found, and Ernest and I soon cut them in half. With these tubs we made a kind of raft, though it was no slight task. The tubs, in fact, were eight small round boats, tied so tightly together that no one of them could float away from the rest. The next thing to be done was to launch the raft. This we finally did, and when the boys saw it slide down the side of the ship and float on the sea, they gave a loud shout, and each one tried who should be the first to get on it. I tied it securely to the ship, and left it there.

I then told my wife to change her clothes and wear some of those left by the crew, as her skirts would have got in her way when she had to climb. She did not like this at first, but did so as soon as she saw the truth of what I told her.

At last, when all was done, we went to bed, and slept as soundly as if we had been on land.

We were all up at the break of day, and knelt down to thank God that He had kept us from harm through the night.

We then put all the things on the raft. Ten live hens and two cocks were put in one of the

tubs. Some ducks and geese
we let go, in the hope that they would swim
to the shore; and a pair of doves were set free,
as they could fly to the land.

There was a place in the raft for each of
us. In the first tub sat my wife; in the next
Franz,[5] who was nearly eight years old; in the
third Fritz, not quite sixteen. In the fourth
were the fowls, and some old sails that would
make us a tent; the fifth was full of good
things in the way of food. In the sixth stood

[5]Franz (fränz)

Jack, a bold lad, ten
years old; in the next
Ernest, thirteen years of age,
well taught, but too fond of himself, and less
fond of work than the rest. I sat in the eighth,
to guide the raft that was to save all that was
dear to me in the world.

As soon as the dogs (Juno and Turk by
name) saw us push off from the ship they
leaped into the sea behind us, and both being
large mastiffs, kept up with us well.

The sea was calm; so that we felt quite
safe. We made good use of the oars, and the

raft bore its freight straight to the land; but as we drew near to the shore the sight of the bare rocks led us to think that we might still be in need of food and drink when that which we had was gone.

As we got near, the coast lost its bare look, and we were glad to see that there was no lack of trees. We soon found a bay, to which the ducks and geese had found their way, and here we saw a place where we could land.

As soon as we had made the raft secure with a strong rope, we took out all our wealth, and made a tent with the old sailcloth we had brought with us, and stuck a pole in the ground to keep it up. This done, I sent the boys to get moss and dry grass to make our beds with. With the flint and steel we soon set fire to some dry twigs, and my wife made a pot of soup with what she had brought from the ship.

Fritz, who had charge of the guns, chose one, and took a stroll by the side of a stream, while Jack went in search of shellfish, which he thought he might find on the rocks. My share of the work was to save two large casks which were near the shore. While I was up to my knees in the sea I heard a shrill cry, which I knew to come from Jack. I got out at once, took up an ax, and ran to help him. I found him with his legs in a rock pool, where a large lobster held him by his toes. It soon made off as I came near; but I struck at it with the ax, and brought it out of the pool. Jack then took it up, though it gave him a pinch or two before he found out how to hold it, and ran off in high glee to show what he had caught.

When I got back to the tent, I found that Ernest had brought us news that he had seen salt in the chinks of the rocks, and that shellfish were not scarce.

"Well, my boy, if you are sure you saw them, I will ask you to go back for some. We must each do some work for the good of all."

He went, and soon found the salt, left by the sea on the rocks, which the sun had made quite dry. There was some sand on it, but my wife did not take long to find a way to cure that. She had been to a fresh stream with a large jug; from this I saw her pour some on the salt, strain it through a cloth, and let it drip in a cup, so that all the sand was left on the cloth.

When the soup was made hot we had each a taste, and all said that it was good.

"Don't be too hasty," said my wife, "we must wait for Fritz; but even if he were here, I do not see how we are to eat our soup, for we have no plates nor spoons."

"If we had some large nuts," said Ernest, "we might cut them in half, and they would make good bowls."

"Quite true," I said, "but there are none."

"Now I have it," replied Ernest. "We can use the oyster shells I saw on the shore."

Off ran Jack to the shore, with Ernest at his heels, and back they both came with large and small shells for us all.

Just then Fritz came in, with a look of gloom on his face, which I could see was a sham.[6]

"You do not mean to tell me you have come back with nothing?" I said, as he put out his hands as if to prove that such was the case. But

---

[6]sham—*something false*

Jack, who had been around behind him, cried out, "No, no! he's got a pig!—such a fine one. Tell us where you found it."

Fritz now brought forth his prize. When I saw it, I knew, from what I had read, that it was not a pig but an agouti,[7] a swift beast, known in these parts, that lives on fruit and nuts, and hides in the earth.

"I like the place much more than I do this spot," he said. "The shore lies low, and there are planks, casks, chests, and all sorts of things, that the sea has thrown up on the shore. Why not leave this place at once, and go there?"

"There is a time for all things," I said. "We must at least rest here for one night."

We all sat down to take our soup with the shell spoons. Ernest took from his coat a large bowl-shaped shell, which he had hid till now, filled it with the soup, and then set it down to cool.

"You are very clever," I said to him. "But I am not glad to see that you think only of

---

[7]agouti (ə·go͞o′tē)

yourself, and do so much for your own ease, when all the rest of us work together. Now, that shell full of soup you must give to our two dogs. We can all dip our small shells in the pot, and you must do as we do."

I knew he felt hurt at this, but he gave it to the dogs at once, and they soon made quick work of their share of the soup.

The sun was low when our meal came to an end. The fowls came round us to pick up the stray crumbs we had let fall, and my wife took out her bag of grain and fed the cocks and hens, and sent them to roost on the top of our tent.

We took care to load our guns, in case we might need them in the night; sang a hymn of praise to God, and then left our fate in His hands.

As soon as I heard the cock crow, and saw by the light that it was morning, I got out of bed and discussed with my wife what we should do next.

"First," I said, "Fritz and I will make a tour of the coast and try to find some of the men who left the ship, for if they are here they may be in need."

"But," said Fritz, who had heard me from his bed, "why should we search for those who left us to die on the wreck?"

"Well, I will tell you," I said. "First, we should do to them as we would wish them to do to us; next, we know that they took no food with them, and we should not leave them to starve; and last, it may be that they can help us, though now they are probably more in need of our aid."

The boys were soon up, and we all sat down to a good meal. That done, Fritz and I got ready to leave. I put a pair of small guns in his belt, gave him a game bag, and told him to take an ax. I took some food for us both, and a full flask out of which we could drink if we should stray far from a stream.

We left the dog Juno to guard the tent, but Turk went with us and ran by our side.

We soon got to the banks of a stream; but then had to make our way down its course. It took us some time to reach the seashore. There was not a boat to be seen, or any sign that the ship's crew had found the land. We left the shore and went through a wood full of tall trees. Here Fritz struck some hard thing on the ground with his foot, which we found to be a coconut. He gave it a blow with his ax, and broke the shell, and we both sat down to rest and eat the nut.

At the end of the wood we came to a plain which gave us a clear view of the place. Fritz, who was on the lookout, ran off with

Turk to some strange tree that he saw on the right.

When I caught up to him, it gave me no small joy to find that it was a gourd tree.

"Try," I said, "if you can get hold of one of those strange lumps that grow on it."

With that he brought one down, and we had a look at it.

"Now, of this," I said, "we can make a plate, a dish, or a flask. Natives of these islands set great store by its shell, which they use to hold their food and drink."

We then set to work to make dishes of the gourds. When we had made some eight or ten bowls, and some flat plates, we laid them out in the sun to dry and then went on our way.

We could see, not far off, a grove of fine palm trees, but to reach them we should have to pass through reeds and long grass. I knew this was just the place to find snakes, so we each cut a cane, that we might beat them off should we meet with any. As I took hold of my staff, I felt a gum or juice ooze out of the end. I put my tongue to it and found that it tasted sweet. This led me to suck the reed, and I then knew that we had met with the sugar cane. By this time Fritz had done the same, for I could see that he held his cane to his mouth.

"Do not suck too much of it," I said, "or it will make you ill; but let's cut some of the best and take them back with us, for those at home will enjoy so great a treat."

It did not take us long to reach the place where the palms grew, and then we sat down in the shade to eat the food we had brought with us.

"Do you see those nuts at the top of the trees, Fritz?" I said.

"To be sure I do; but they are far too high

to reach. Look, look!" he cried, "there are some monkeys; let me have a shot at them."

"Don't do that," I said, and held his arm; "it will do us no good to kill them,

and I think I can make use
of them." With that I threw
some stones up at the tree where
they were, though they had got
safe out of my reach. They then
made a loud noise, took hold of the
nuts that were near, and flung them
straight at us. The trick made Fritz
laugh, who soon had hard work
to pick up the nuts that were
thrown at him.

We broke some of
the nuts, and put the
juice of the canes

in the thick white cream which forms close to the shell; and this made us a dish that Fritz said was fit for a king.

Fritz and I then tied some nuts to a string, which I tied round my waist, while he took up the canes, and we both set off on our way home.

On our way back we took up the gourd bowls and plates, which we found quite dry and hard as bone, and put them in our bags. We had scarcely gotten through the wood, when Turk darted in front of us, and we saw a troop of apes rush out of the way. But he gave a leap and brought down one that could not climb so fast as the rest, for she had a young one in her arms. Before Fritz could call the dog off, the mother ape was dead. The young one, as soon as it saw Fritz, sprang on his back, put its paws in his curls, and would not let go. I at length got the ape from Fritz's back, and took it up in my arms like a child. We found that it was too young to seek its own food, and, as Fritz said he should like to take it home, we put it on Turk's back. Turk did not at first like this, but we soon got him to carry the ape, which held so tightly to the hair on the dog's neck that it could not fall off. Fritz then led Turk with a string, that he might not stray out of sight, or throw off his charge, which I think he would have done had we not been on the watch.

It did not take us long to reach the bank of the stream near our home.

I need not tell you how glad my wife and sons were to see us back safely, or with what joy the boys took the "real live ape" out of Fritz's arms.

At length, when they settled down, I told them we had brought them all sorts of good things, but that we had not met with any of the men of whom we went in search. "God's will be done," said my wife, "let us thank Him that you have come back safely to us. This day to me has been an age; but put down your loads, for we must now go in and hear what you have to tell."

Fritz and I then told them, by turns, where we found the things we brought with us, how we made and dried the plates and bowls, cut the canes, and caught the ape in the woods.

Our tales had not come to an end when we were told that it was time for supper. Ernest had shot a wild goose, and some fish had been caught in the stream. With these and the Dutch cheese that we brought from the ship, we made a good meal; but the boys would not rest till we broke some of the coconuts, from which they drank the milk, made sweet with the juice of the sugar cane. I must tell you that we greatly enjoyed eating our food from our gourd rind plates, which my wife said she should prize more than if they were made of pure gold.

That night the ape went to bed with Jack and Fritz, and we all slept in peace till the cocks on the roof of the tent woke us up.

Next day Fritz and I went back to the wreck to save the livestock, and get what else we had left that might be of use to us. We found it no light task, for we had to make floats for the cow, the donkey, the sheep, and the goats, throw them in the sea, and tie them with ropes to our raft. We put on board the raft a vast deal of food that had not been spoiled by the sea, though the waves had broken through the sides of the wreck. We then set out for shore with our train of livestock tied securely to the stern.

We had not gone far when I heard a loud cry of fear from Fritz, "We are lost! We are lost! Look at that great shark on its way to us!"

Though pale with fright, he took aim with his gun, and shot the fish in the head. It sank at once, which I knew to be a sign that we were once more safe. We then got to land, and secured our freight to the shore. Before we had done this our family came to give us what help they could to get the beasts out of the stream, and take them up to the tent. The poor animals were well nigh worn out; but we took good care of them, and put them to rest on some dry grass that my wife had laid out for them.

That night we did not eat on the ground. My wife had spread a cloth on the top of a cask, and we each sat on a tub. With the knives and forks that we had found in the ship we ate a dish of hot ham and eggs.

Before bedtime my wife told me that while I was at the wreck she had gone in search of some place in which we could build a house.

"And did you find one, my dear?" I said.

"Oh, yes," she said. "We can take you to a great tree that will serve us well, if we can but get across the stream with our goods."

"But would you have us roost, like fowls, in a tree? How do you think we could get up to our perch?"

"Was there not a large lime tree in our town in which they built a ballroom, with stairs up the trunk?"

"To be sure there was," I said; "and if we cannot build in it, we can at least make use of its shade, and dwell in a hut on the roots."

Ernest said that he took a string and found that it was twelve yards around the trunk. This led me to think that my wife's scheme was by no means a bad one, and that I would have a look at the tree the next day.

When I had heard all they had to tell, we knelt down to pray, and then sought a good night's rest, which the toils of the day made us much in need of.

Chapter 3
The Tree House

When I rose from my bed the next day, I said to my wife, "Does it not seem, my dear, as if God had led us to this place, and that we should do wrong to leave it?"

"What you say may be quite true, so far as it goes," she said. "But I must tell you that the midday heat is more than we can bear, and that if we stay here we may have to keep watch at night. There are, no doubt, wild beasts of some kind that will find us; and we should not trust our dogs too much; they may lose their lives in a fight with them."

"I dare say you are right," I said; "but I do not yet see how we can cross the stream. We shall first have to build a bridge."

The boys were now all out of their beds; and while my wife went to milk the cow and cook some food, I made my plans known to them. They were all glad when they heard that we were to leave our tent on the beach, and each said he would help to build the bridge.

The first thing to be done was to find some strong planks;[8] and Fritz, Ernest, and I went down to the shore, and got in the boat, which the tide took down to the bay.

On a piece of land which lay to the left we could see some large dark thing, round which flew a flock of sea gulls. We put up a sail and caught a gust of wind which had sprung up, and this soon brought the boat to the spot. We made no noise, but crept up the shore step by step. Fritz was the first to realize that what we had found was the huge shark he had shot in the sea. We cut off some rough skin, which we thought might serve for files,[9] and then went back to the boat. I glanced back at the shore before I got in, and to my great joy saw some

---

[8] plank—*a thick piece of lumber*
[9] file—*a tool used for cutting*

of the planks and poles from the wreck lying on the ground not far off. Our next task was to bind these so as to make a raft, which we tied to the stern of the boat, and then, by the use of our oars, soon made our way up the stream to the place where the bridge was to be built. The others were glad to see us back so soon, and ran to meet us; Jack had a cloth in his hand, in which was a store of crayfish and crabs just caught in some of the nooks of a rock up the stream.

"Do not fail to give God thanks," I said, "that He has placed us where we can pick up more food than we can eat."

It would take a long time to tell how we brought all the wood up to the spot, built layers of stones in the stream, and put the planks one by one in place; it was late at night when we left off work and once more sought our tent.

The next day we saw the sun rise, and took our first meal in haste, for we knew we should have a long day's toil. All the supplies that we could not take with us were left in the tent, the door of which was made safe by a row of casks, that we put round it. My wife and Fritz soon led the way; the cow went next; then the donkey, with Franz on its back. Jack led the goats, and on the back of one of them sat the ape. Ernest took charge of the sheep, and I brought up the rear as chief guard. We took care to cross the bridge one at a time, and found it bore our weight well; but once or twice we thought the cow would step in the stream, or fall off the boards, when she went to the sides to drink.

Just as we had left the bridge, Jack cried out, "Be quick! Here is a strange beast with quills as long as my arm." The dogs ran, and I with them, and found a large porcupine in the grass. It made a loud noise, and shoved its quills at the dogs, making them bleed. At this Jack shot at the beast, which fell dead on the spot. My wife's first thought was to dress the wounds made by the quills, which had stuck in the nose of one of the dogs, while the boys made haste to pluck some of the quills from the skin of their strange prize.

At last our march came to an end, and I saw for the first time the great trees that my wife had told me of. They were of vast size and were, I thought, fig trees. "If we can but fix our tent up there," I said, "we shall have no cause to dread, for no wild beasts can reach us." We sent Franz off to find sticks with which to make a fire, and my wife made some soup of the flesh of the porcupine, though we did not like it so well as we did the ham and cheese we brought with us.

When the meal ended, my first thought was to make some steps by means of which we could reach the first strong branch of the tree.

Ernest and I went in search of some thick canes that grew in the sands nearby. These we cut down, bound them to four long poles, and thus made a pair of steps that would, we thought, reach far up the trunk.

On our way back from the sands, one of the dogs made a dart at a clump of reeds, and a troop of birds rose on the wing with a loud noise. Fritz took aim at them and brought down one which, though hurt in the wing, made use of its long legs so well that it would have got off if Juno had not held it. The joy of Fritz to have caught such a strange bird was so great that he suggested at once that we bind it by the neck and take it back with us. "Look," said Ernest, "what fine plumes he has, and you see he has webbed feet like a goose, and has long legs like a stork; thus he can run on land as fast as he can swim."

"Yes," I said, "and he can fly with more speed through the air, for these birds have great strength in their wings. In fact, few birds have such means of flight as the flamingo."

My wife thought the great bird might need more food than we could spare. I told her that it would feed on small fish and worms and not rob our geese of their grain. I then tied him to a stake near the stream; and in a few days we were glad to find that he knew us, and would come at a call, like a tame bird.

While I sat on the grass with my sons, late in the day, I thought I would try to make a bow and thus save our shot. This I did with a long cane and a piece of string, and then made a dart with a sharp point, which I shot off and found it would go straight. The branch of the tree on which we were to fix our hut was so high that our steps would not near reach it. I tied some strong thread to the dart, and shot it over the branch; then tied a piece of rope to the end of the thread, and drew that up, and at last made a long row of cane steps, with a rope at each side, which we drew up the first strong branch. The boys were now all in haste to climb the tree, but I chose that Jack, who was light of build and sure of foot, should go up first and try the strength of our work. Fritz went up next with some nails, and secured the ropes to the tree, while I drove stakes in the ground to keep them firm at the foot. It was now time for me to climb the ladder, and up I went with an ax to chop off the twigs and smooth the branch that was to form the ground of our new house. I sent the boys down out of my way and kept hard at work till it was late, for the sky was clear and the moon lent me her beams of light to see by.

When I came down, my wife spread a good meal on the ground, which we ate as best we could, and then made our beds of dry moss, round which we put heaps of twigs. These we set on fire, to keep off wild beasts and snakes. The toils of the day had made the boys tired, and they were soon in a sound sleep, but my wife and I took turns watching through the whole night.

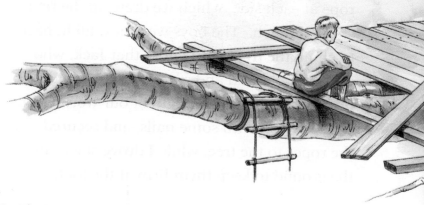

We were all out of bed as soon as light was in the sky, and we set to work hoisting up the planks that were to form the floor of our hut. These we laid down on the branch, with their ends nailed to a crosspiece of wood that we had to fix to the trunk of the tree. Our nails were long, and we drove each one of them home, so that we had no cause to fear the strength of our work. By the time we had

done this the day was far spent, and we were all glad to lay down our tools and rest. That night we lit our fires around the tree, tied the dogs to the roots, and went up to sleep out of harm's way for the first time since we left the ship. When the steps were drawn up we all felt that we were now safe at last and that we had brought the toils of the day to a good end.

Chapter 4
A Day of Rest

We did not wake the next day till the sun shone in upon us. I told my wife and sons that as it was the Lord's day we would do no work. Our beasts and birds had to be fed first. This was done by my wife, who then brought us some hot food, and made us sit down on the grass and take it. When our meal was done, I stood on a log in front of my sons, and we all sang a psalm we knew by heart. Then I began to teach them, and spoke to them thus:

"There once was a Great King, who had two vast realms, the Land of Light and Truth, and the Land of Night and Sloth. Those who dwelt in the first were full of life and joy. The King lived at the Place of Rest, where all was bright.

"This King had a land, not far off, where those he loved should dwell before they went one by one to the Place of Rest. This land was the Home of Earth. He gave to his Son the right to rule the people that dwelt in the Home of Earth, and instruct them in what they were to do and all the ills that would come to them if they did not do as they were told.

"At first they were all glad to hear the way in which they were to live and the terms on which they could reach the Land of Light and Truth. Sad to tell, they soon broke the King's laws, and paid no heed to what they knew to be his will. Still there were a few who did as they had been taught and dwelt in peace, in the hope that they would please the King.

"From time to time ships came to the Home of Earth, and at last a great ship was sent, the name of which was *The Grave*, which bore the flag of *Death*. To those who had obeyed the King it was a sign of hope, but the others were thrown into a state of gloom at the sight of it. This ship was not seen till it came close to the shore, and then the crew were sent forth to find those whom they were told to seize. Some went back with them full of joy, but most were seen to weep and mourn their fate. As soon as they were brought in sight of the Great King, the Prince took those who had obeyed, and put a white robe on them; but those who went their own way when on the Home of Earth he sent down into deep, dark mines for all eternity."

When my sons had heard my tale to the end they all knew what it meant; I then drew from them their views of what it meant to serve the Great King. We then sang a hymn; and my wife drew from her bag the Bible, which I gave to one of the boys, who read from it in a clear, loud voice. When this was brought to a close, we all knelt down on the grass to pray, and to ask God to bless us as we sought to learn His will.

We did no work that day, but took a long stroll up the banks of the stream. Ernest and Jack tried their skill with the bow. I gave them permission to kill what they could; for I knew if the meat was put in casks made air tight with grease, it would keep for a time, and might prove useful, if our stock of food should get low.

When we sat down to dine, the thought struck me that it would be good to give some name to each part of the island that was known to us. This was at first the source of some fun, for Fritz said we should call the bay where we had found the oyster shell spoons by the name of Oyster Bay; but Jack, who still had a mark on his toe where the lobster gave him a pinch, thought we ought to call it Lobster Bay.

"If you will let me give it a name," said my wife, "I should wish to know it by some name that will remind us how good God was to lead our raft there, and I think Safety Bay will be a good name for it."

"So let it be," I said; and from that time Safety Bay had a name.

"What shall be the name of the spot where we spent our first night on shore? You shall give that its name," I said to Fritz.

"Let us call it Tentholm."

"That will do," I said.

The place from which Fritz and I sought in vain for a trace of our shipmates was to be known as Cape Disappointment. Then we had

The Boys' Bridge, which name I gave it from a wish to please my sons, who had done so much to build it.

"But what shall we call our treetop home which is most dear to us all?"

"Now, my dear," I said to my wife, "it is your turn. What shall we say?"

"Let us call it Falconhurst," she said. "It is much like our own little nest."

When the heat of the day was past, I told my sons that I should be glad to take a walk with them. My wife said that she should like to go with us; so we left The Nest (as we came to call it) in charge of Turk, and turned our course to the banks of the stream. On our way we went past some shrubs and rare herbs which my wife knew well how to make use of should we fall sick, and Ernest found a large spot of ground on which grew a fine kind of potato. At these the boys set to work with such zeal that we soon had a bag full of the ripe fruit. We then went on to Tentholm, which we found in the same state as when we left it to cross the stream on our way to the great tree.

We found that our ducks and geese had grown so wild that they would not come near us; so, while my wife and I went to pick up such things as we thought we might take back with us, Ernest and Fritz were sent to catch them and to tie their legs and wings, and in this way we got them at last to The Nest.

Chapter 5

Useful Discoveries

I t took the whole of the next day to make a sledge,[10] to which we tied the donkey, and drove to Tentholm. On our sledge we put such of the casks which held food, and took them back to The Nest. Fritz and I went once more to the wreck, and this time we brought off chests of clothes, blocks of lead, cart wheels, sacks of maize,[11] oats, peas, and wheat. With a strong bar we broke down some of the doors, and took such parts of the ship as we thought would aid us to build our house, which as yet was far less safe than I could wish. These we bound with

[10]sledge—*a vehicle that has low runners instead of wheels*
[11]maize—*corn*

cords, and made them float back at the stern of the raft.

When we got to the shore my wife and the three boys were there to greet us. My first job was to send for the sledge, and with this we took most of our new wealth up to The Nest.

The next day I told my sons that they must now learn to run, to leap, to climb, and to throw stones straight at a mark, as all these things would be of great use to them in their new mode of life.

I next taught them to use the lasso, by means of which men catch the wild horse on the vast plains of the New World. I tied two stones to the ends of a cord some yards in length and flung off one of them at the trunk of a young tree. The cord went round and round the tree in a coil, and bound it so tight that I could have drawn it to me had it not been rooted in the ground. This trick the boys were quick to learn; and Fritz, in a short time, could take an aim as well with a stone as he could with his gun.

As yet we had not seen much of the isle, for it took most of our time to build the house.

But one day we made up our minds that we would all start on a tour. We rose at dawn, put the donkey in the sledge, took what food we thought we should need, and set out from Falconhurst just as the sun rose.

When we came to the wood where Fritz found the ape, he explained how we had gotten the coconuts, but now there were no apes there to throw them down.

"Oh, if one would but fall from the trees," he said.

The words had but just left his lips when a large nut fell at his feet. He jumped back, and two more came down near the same spot.

As the nuts were far from ripe, I was at a loss to know how they could fall off the tree, for I could not see an ape nor a bird near.

I went up close to the tree and saw a large land crab on its way down the trunk. Jack struck a blow at him with a stick, but did not hit the beast. He then took off his coat and threw it on the crab's head, while I made an end of him with an ax. I told them that these crabs climb the trees and break off the nuts, as we had seen, and then come down to feast on them at their ease.

"But how do they crack the nuts?" said Jack.

"They make a hole through the shell at the thin end and then suck them dry."

The dead crab was put in the sledge, and we went on through the wood. When we came to the Gourd Wood, we sat down to make some more bowls and flasks to take back with us. Ernest had gone to see what new things he could find, but he had not been away long, when we heard him call out—

"A wild boar! A great wild boar! Come here!"

We took up our guns and went at once with the dogs to the spot. We soon heard Turk give a loud bark, and just then we heard Ernest laugh and saw the two dogs come through a clump of brush wood, with our old sow fast by the ears. She did not seem to like the way in which they had put an end to her feast of fruit, so she ran back as soon as we told the dogs to let go their hold of her ears.

"But with all our sport," said Fritz, "we have a poor show of game. Let us leave the young ones, and set off to see what we can find." Ernest sat down with Franz, and we left them and my wife at the gourd tree, while Fritz and

Jack set off with me to a high rock which we saw on the right.

"Fritz, look here," said Jack, as he made his way to the rock.

"What have you found now?" said Fritz.

"I don't know what it is, but it's a fine prize."

When I went up I saw at once that it was a large iguana, the flesh and eggs of which are both good for food. I had heard that these and other similar beasts will stand still if you play music on a pipe. So I crept near and made a low sound with my lips, while I held in my right hand a stout stick to which I had tied a cord with a noose.

I saw it first move its tail and then draw its head from side to side, as if to look where the sound came from. I then threw the noose around its neck, drew it tight, got on its back with a leap and swiftly killed it. Our prize, which was nearly five feet long, was no slight weight to lift. I got it at last on my back, and thus we went back to the gourd tree.

It took us a long time to reach home that night. My wife did her best to cook some of the flesh of the land crab, but it was tough and did not taste so nice as the soup made from the iguana that we had caught.

Fritz and I spent the whole of the next day in the woods. We took the donkey and one of the dogs with us, but left all else at home.

Our way first lay through a dense wood, where we saw no end of small birds, but such game could not now tempt Fritz to waste his shot. We then had to cross a vast plain and to wade through the high grass, which we did with care, in fear that we should tread on some strange animal that might turn and bite us.

We came at last to a grove of small trees, and in their midst I saw a bush, which I knew to be the wax tree, for the wax grew on it like white beads. I need not say how glad I was to find so great a prize. We had up to this time gone to bed as soon as the sun went down, for we had no lamp to use; but as we could now make wax lights, I told Fritz that we had found what would add two or three hours per day to our lives. We took as much of the wax as would serve us for some time and then made our way out of the grove.

"How came you," said Fritz, "to know so much of the animals, trees, and plants that we have found here?"

"When I was young," I said, "I used to read all the books that came my way; and those that told of strange lands and what was to be seen in them had for me as great a charm as they have for Ernest, who has read a great deal and knows more of plants than you do."

"Well," he said, "I will do the same if I get the chance. Do you know the name of that huge tree on the right? See, there are balls on the bark."

We went close to it and found that these balls were of thick gum, which the sun had made quite hard. Fritz tried to pull one of them off, but felt that it clung tightly to the bark, though he could change its shape with his warm hands. "Look," he said, "I feel sure that this is the India rubber which we used to clean our school books."

I took a piece of it in my hand, and said, "To be sure it is. What shall we not find in this rich land?" I then told him how the men in the New World made flasks of this gum, in which form it is sent to all parts of the world. "And I do not see why we should not make boots of it in the same way. We have but to fill a sock with sand, then put gum all around it, while in a soft state, till it is as thick as we need. We then pour the sand out, and we shall have made a shoe or a boot that will at least keep out the damp, and this is more than mine do just now."

Not far from this we came to a bush, the leaves of which were strewn with a white dust; and close by were two or three more in the same state. I cut a slit in the trunk of one of these and found it full of the white dust, which I knew by the taste to be sago.[12] We took all of this that we could get out of the tree, for

---

[12]sago—*a type of starch used to thicken foods*

it would add to our stock of food; and when our bags were full we laid them on the back of the donkey and set off to find our way back to The Nest.

"Each day brings us fresh wealth," said my wife; "but I think we might now try to add to our goods." I knew that she had some fear lest we should one day get lost in the woods or meet with wild beasts, so I at once said that we would now stay at home, at least for some days.

My first work was to make some wax lights, for my wife could mend our clothes at night while we sat down to talk. This done, the next task they gave me was to make a churn. I took a large gourd, made a small hole in the side, and cut out as much as I could, so as to leave only the rind. In this I put the cream, plugged the hole, and bound it up so that none could come out. The boys then held a cloth, and on it I put the gourd, which they rolled from side to side. They kept up this game with great mirth for nearly an hour, when my wife took off the string, and found that the churn had done its work well.

As our sledge was not fit to use on rough roads, my next work was to make a cart. I had brought a pair of wheels from the wreck, so my task did not prove a hard one.

While I was thus at work, my wife and the boys took some of the fruit trees we had brought with us and put them in the ground where they thought they would grow best. On each side of the path that led from The Nest to The Boys' Bridge they put a row of young nut trees. To make the path hard we laid down sand from the seashore, and then beat it down with our spades.

We spent six weeks at this and similar work. We did not spare any pains to make The Nest, and all that could be seen near it, look neat and trim, though there were no eyes but our own to view the scene.

One day I told my sons that I would try to make a flight of stairs in place of the cane steps with rope sides, which were, to tell the truth, the worst part of our house. As yet we had not used them much, but the rain would some day force us to stay inside The Nest, and then we should like to go up and down stairs with more ease than we could now climb the rude steps. I knew that a swarm of bees had built their nest in the trunk of our tree, and this led me to think that there might be a void space in it some way up. "Should this prove to be the case," I said, "our work will be half done, for we shall then only need to fix the stairs in the tree around the trunk." The boys got up and went to the top of the root to tap the trunk and to judge by the sound how far up the hole went. But they had to pay for their lack of thought; the whole swarm of bees came out as soon as they heard the noise. The bees stung their cheeks, stuck to their hair and clothes, and soon put them to flight.

We found that Jack, who was at all times rash, had struck the bees' nest with his ax and was much more hurt by them than the rest. Ernest, who went to his work in his slow way, got up to the tree last and thus did not get more than a sting or two, but for the rest it was several hours before they could see out of their eyes. I took a large hollow gourd, which would make a perfect hive, and put it on a stand. We then made a straw roof for the hive to keep out the sun and wind, and as by this time it grew dark, we left the hive there for the night.

The next day, the boys, whose wounds were not quite well, went with me to move the bees to the new home we had made for them. Our first work was to stop with clay all the holes in the tree but one through which the bees went into their nest. I put a hollow reed through this hole and sent in the smoke of burning weeds as fast as I could. At first we heard a loud buzz like the noise of a storm afar off; but as the smoke filled the tree, the sound grew less, till at last the bees were quite still.

We now cut out a piece of the trunk, three feet square, and this gave us a full view of the nest. Our joy was great to find such a stock of wax, for I could see the comb reached far up the tree. I took some of the comb, in which the bees lay in swarms, and set it aside.

We then put the gourd on the comb that held the swarm, and took care that the queen bee was not left out. By this method we soon preserved the whole hive of fine bees, and the trunk of the tree was left free for our use.

We had now to try the length of the hole. This we did with a long pole and found it reached as far up as the branch on which our house stood.

We then cut a square hole in the side of the trunk facing the seashore and made one of the doors that we had brought from the ship to fit in the space. We then made the insides of the tree trunk smooth all the way up, and with planks and the staves of some old casks, built up the stairs around a pole which we anchored in the ground. To do this we had to make a notch in the pole and one in the side of the trunk for each stair, and thus go step by step till we came to the top. Each day we spent a part of our time at what we could now call the farm, where the beasts and fowls were kept, so that we should not work too hard on the flight of stairs, which took us some six weeks to put up.

One day Fritz caught a fine eagle which he tied by the leg to a branch of a tree and fed. It took the eagle a long while to become tame, but in time Fritz taught it to perch on his wrist and to feed from his hand. He once let it go and thought he would have lost it, but the bird knew it had a good friend, for it came back to the tree at night. From that time it was left free, though we thought that some day its love of war and wild sports would tempt it to leave us for the rocks of the seashore where Fritz had found it.

Each of my boys had now some pet to take care of, and, I may say, to tease, for they all thought they had a fair right to get some fun out of the pets they could call their own; but they were kind to them, fed them well, and kept them clean.

In what I may term my spare time, which was when I left off work out of doors, I made a pair of gum shoes for each of my sons, in the way I had told Fritz it could be done. I do not know what we should have done had we not found the gum tree, for the stones soon wore out the boots we had, and we could not have gone through the woods or trod the hard rocks with bare feet.

By this time our sow had brought forth ten young pigs, and the hens had each a brood of fine chicks. Some we kept near us, but most of them went to the woods, where my wife said she could find them when she had need to use them.

I knew the time must now be near when, in this part of the world, the rain comes down day by day for weeks, and I thought it might wash us out of The Nest if we did not make a good roof to our house. Then our livestock would need some place where they could rest out of the rain. The thatch for The Nest was of course our first care; then we made a long roof of canes for our livestock, and on this we spread clay and moss and then a thick coat of tar, so that it was rain proof from end to end. This was held up by thick canes stuck deep in the ground, with planks nailed to them to form walls, and around the structure we put a row of cask staves to serve for fence rails. In this way we soon had a barn, storeroom, and hayloft, with stalls for the cow, the donkey, and what else we kept that had need of a place in which to live.

Chapter 6

The Rainy Season

Franz one day found some long leaves, to which, from their shape, he gave the name of sword leaves. These he brought home to play with and then, when he grew tired of them, threw them down. As they lay on the floor, Fritz took some of them in his hand and found them so limp that he could plait[13] them and make a whip for Franz to drive the sheep and goats with. As he split them up to do this, I could not but note their strength. This led me to try them, and I found that we had now a kind of flax plant, which was a source of great joy to my wife.

---

[13]plait—*braid*

"You have not yet found anything," she said, "that will be of more use to us than this. Go at once and search for some more of these leaves, and bring me the most you can of them. With these I can make you leggings, shirts, thread, rope; in short, give me flax and make me a loom[14] and some frames, and I shall be at no loss for work when the rain comes."

I could not help but smile at my wife's joy when she heard the name of flax; for there was still much to do before the leaves could take the shape of cloth. But two of the boys set off at once to try to find some more of the flax.

While they were gone, my wife, full of new life and with some show of pride, told me how I should make the loom on which she was to weave the cloth. In a short time the boys came back and brought with them a good load of the plant, which they laid at her feet. She now said she would set aside all else till she had tried what she could make of it.

---

[14]loom—*a machine used to make thread*

The first thing to be done was to steep the flax. To do this we took the plant down to the marsh, tied up in small bales. The leaves were then spread out in the pond and kept down with stones. They were left there till it was time to take them out and set them in the sun to dry, when they would be so soft that we could peel them with ease. It was two weeks before the flax was fit for us to take out of the marsh. We spread it out on the grass in the sun, where it dried so quickly that we took it home to The Nest the same day. It was then put away till we could find time to make the wheels, reels, and combs which my wife said that she would need to turn our new found plant to its best use.

We now made haste to lay up a supply of canes, nuts, wood, and such things as we thought we might want. And we took care, while the weather was still fine, to sow wheat, and all the grain we had left in our bags was soon put in the ground. The fear that the rain might come and put a stop to our work led us to take our meals in haste and to make the days last as long as we could. We knew the rain was close at hand, for the nights were cold; large clouds could be seen in the sky, and the wind blew as we had not felt it since the night our ship had struck on the rock.

The great change came at last. One night we were waked out of our sleep with the noise made by the rush of the wind through the woods, and we could hear the loud roar of the sea far off. Then the dense storm clouds which we had seen in the sky burst upon us, and the rain came down in floods. The streams, pools, and ponds on all sides were soon full, and the whole plain around us looked like one vast lake. The site of our house stood up out of the flood, and our group of trees had the look of a small island in the midst of the lake.

We soon found that The Nest was not built as well as we thought, for the rain came in at the sides, and we had good cause to fear that the wind would blow the roof off. Once the storm made such a rush at it that we heard the beams creak, and the planks gave signs that there was more strain on them than they could bear. This drove us from our room

to the stairs in the trunk, on which
we sat in a state of fear till
the worst of the storm
was past. Then we went
down to the shed we
had built on the
ground at the root of
the tree. All our sup-
plies were kept here,
so that the space was
too small to hold us,
and the smell from the
beasts made it far from
a fit place for six of us to
dwell; but it was at least
safe for a time, and safety
was of course the first thing
to be thought of. To cook
our food we had to make a fire in the barn, and
as there was no place to let out the smoke, it
got down our throats and made us cough all
day long.

It was now for the first time that my wife
gave a sigh for her old Swiss home. But we all
knew that it was of no use to grieve, and each

set to work to do all he could to make the place look neat and clean. Some of our supplies we took up the stairs out of our way, and this gave us more room. As we had cut square holes in the trunk of the tree all the way up and put in frames of glass that we got from the ship, my wife could sit on the stairs, with Franz at her feet, and mend our clothes. Each day I drove from the barn such beasts as could bear to be out in the rain. That we might not lose them, I tied bells round their necks; and if we found that they did not come back when the sun went down, Fritz and I went out to bring them in. We often got wet through to the skin, which gave us a chill and might have laid us up if my wife had not made cloth capes and hoods for us to wear. To make these rain proof, I spread some of the gum on them while hot. This had the look of oil cloth and kept the head, arms, chest, and back dry. Our gum boots came far up our legs, so that we could go out in the rain and come back quite free from cold and damp.

We made only a few fires, for the air was not cold, save for an hour or two late at night, and we did not cook more than we could help, but ate the dried meat, fowls, and fish we had.

The care of our beasts took us a great part of the day; then we made our cakes and set them to bake in a tin plate on a slow fire. I had cut a hole in the wall to give us light, and put a pane of glass in it to keep out the wind, but the thick clouds hid the sun from the earth, and the shade of the tree threw a gloom around our barn, so that our daylight was short, and night came on far too soon. We then made use of our wax lights and all sat around a bench. My wife had all she could do to mend the tears we made in our clothes. I kept a log,[15] in which I put down, day by day, what we did and what we had seen; and then Ernest wrote this out in a neat, clear hand and made a book of it. Fritz and Jack drew the plants, trees, and beasts which they had found, and these were stuck in our book. Each night we took turns to read the Word of God, and then all knelt down to pray before we went to bed. Ours was not a life of ease, it is true, but it was one of peace and

---

[15]log—*a record of events*

hope; and we felt that God had been so kind to us that it would be a great sin to wish for what it did not please Him to grant us.

My wife did all she could to cheer us, and it was no strange thing for us to find that while we were out in the rain with the livestock, she had made some new dish, which we could smell as soon as we put our heads in at the door. One night it was a thrush pie, the next a roast fowl, or some wild duck soup; and once in a while she would give us a grand feast and bring out some of all the good things we had in store.

In the course of our stay indoors we made up our minds that we would not spend the next season of storm and rain in the same place. The Nest would serve us well in that time of year when it was fine and dry, but we should have to look out for some spot where we could build a house that would keep us from the rain the next time the storms came.

Fritz thought that we might find a cave, or cut one out of the rocks by the seashore. I told him that this would be a good plan, but would take a long time to do. By this time the boys were all well used to hard work, and they thought they would much like to try their skill at some new kind of work.

"Well," I said, "we will go to the rocks round Tentholm the first fine day that comes, and try to find some place that will serve to keep us from the next year's storms."

Chapter 7

The Salt Cavern

I cannot tell how glad we all were when we at last saw a change in the sky and felt once more the warm rays of the sun. In a few days the floods sank in the earth and left the ground of a bright green hue; the air grew warm and dry, and there were no more dark clouds to be seen in the sky.

We found our young trees had put forth new leaves, and the seed we had sown had come up through the moist ground. The air had a fresh sweet smell, for it bore the scent of the blooms which hung like snowflakes on the boughs of the fruit trees. The songs and cries of the birds were to be heard on all sides, and we could see them fly from tree to tree in search of twigs to build their nests. This in fact was the spring of the year, when all things put forth new life; and we knew that the time was now come when we could once more roam the woods and till the soil, and this made the boys leap for joy.

Some planks had been blown off the roof of The Nest, and the rain had got in here and there; so our first job was to mend our house and make it fit to sleep in.

This done, Jack, Fritz, and I set out to Tentholm. We found it in a sad state. The storm had thrown down the tent, blown off some of the sailcloth, and let in the rain on our casks, some of which held a store of food. Our boat was still safe, but the raft of tubs had broken up, and what was left of it lay in pieces on the shore.

Our loss in the storm had been so great that I felt we ought at once to seek for some place on the rocks where we could put what was left.

We went all round the cliffs, in the hope that we might find a cave, but in vain.

"There is no way but to hew one out of the rock," said Fritz, "for we must not be beat."

"Well said, Fritz," said Jack; "we each have an ax. Why not try this cliff at once?"

I gave them permission to try, and we soon set to work at the rock. From this spot we had a good view of the whole bay and could see both banks of the stream.

With a piece of chalk I made a mark on the side of the cliff to show the width and height that the cave should be cut. Then each took an ax to test what kind of stuff our rock was made of. We found it a hard kind of stone; and, as we were not used to this sort of work, we had not done much when the time came for us to quit.

We came back the next day and got on with more speed, though we thought it would not take us less than six months to make the cave, if our work were done at the same rate each day.

At the end of five or six days we had got through the face of the rock, and we found the stone soft. In a day or two more we came to what was but hard clay, which gave way at a slight blow from the ax.

"We need not fear now," I said, "for we shall soon have a hole as large as we want."

With the earth we took out we made a
ridge in front of the cliff. The boys now got on
so well, and dug so much out, that I had hard
work to throw up the earth on the bank.

One day, as Jack stuck his ax in at the
back of the cave, a great mass of the rock
fell in. "I have broken through!" he shouted
excitedly. "My ax went right through the rock;
I heard it crash down inside. Oh, do come
and see!"

Fritz and I went up the wall and I thrust
the handle of my ax into the hole he spoke of.
It touched nothing on any side. Fritz handed
me a long pole with which to try the depth.
I could feel nothing. I then concluded that a
thin wall was all that stood between us and a
great cavern.

With shouts of joy, the boys battered at
the rock until the hole was large enough for
us to enter. Jack's first thought was to jump
in; but as I suspected that the stagnant air of
the cave might be poisonous, I would not let
him risk his life.

The boys then set fire to some hay and
thrust it in the hole, but it went out at once,

which was a sure sign that the air was not fit to breathe.

I knew that we had brought from the wreck a box full of signal rockets, and I sent Fritz to Tentholm for these. When he came back, I set light to some of them and threw them in the hole. They flew around and threw out a stream of sparks that lit up the cave. When these were burnt out, we put in another heap of burning straw. This was soon in a blaze, indicating that the air was now purified.

Our joy was so great that we sent Jack off home to The Nest to tell the good news and to bring back some wax lights. I did not deem it safe for us to go in the cave in the dark, for there might be pools or deep dry pits in the ground.

Fritz and I had just thrown up on the bank the last spade full of earth that had been dug out when we heard a loud shout. We got up on the top of the cave, and saw that Jack had brought back a tribe at his heels. The large cart, drawn by the cow and the donkey, came on at a slow pace, led by Jack on a black ox, and in it were my wife, Franz, and Ernest.

By the help of a flint and steel I soon lit some of the wax lights and gave one to each. I went in first and led the way, and the rest kept close at my back. We had not gone on more than a few steps when we came to a dead stop, struck with awe at the grand sight that met our view. The walls and roof of the cave were lit up, as it were, with starlike gems, while some

hung down like glass drops from the roof, and some rose up from the ground at its sides. I broke off a piece and put it on my tongue.

"What does it taste like?" said Jack.

"I find," I said, "that we are in a cave of rock salt."

"We shall not have to scrape the rocks to get our salt now," said Ernest, "for there is more here than would serve a whole town for a lifetime."

When we went back to Falconhurst that night we laid out a plan for our new home, for there could be no doubt that the cave was the best place for us to dwell in, though we would still sleep in The Nest when we went on that side of the stream.

The next day we all set to work. The floor of the cave was quite smooth, and the walls dry, so that we could build at once. We first cut holes in the sides of the rock to let in the light, and then brought frames and panes of glass from The Nest and put them in. We then brought all the planks and wood we could find and built a strong wall in the midst of the cave. On the right side of this wall we made three rooms, two of which were to be used as bedrooms, and one to take our meals in. On the left side was a room for my wife to cook in, one to work in, to which we gave the name of the shop, and a place with stalls in it for our livestock. At the back of these was a store-house, where we could keep our stock of food and all of our spare goods.

I need not say that it took us some months to do all this, nor that we had to toil hard day by day; but the end did come at last, and then the joy we felt that we had done all this with our own hands more than paid us for our toil.

Chapter 8

The Farm

Our fields near Tentholm had by this time brought forth good crops of wheat, maize, beans, and peas; but as the work of the cave had for some weeks kept us on this side of the stream, we did not know in what state we should find our crops at The Nest.

One day we all set out for our old home. We found our cornfields of a rich brown color, and saw that the wheat was, for the most part, fit to reap. This and a large patch of rye we cut down, and, as we did so, whole flocks of birds took wing when we got near them, while quails were seen to run off at the sight of our dogs, who had no lack of sport that day.

We set aside the seed that was quite ripe till the time should come for us to sow it and put the rest in sacks. Some of the wheat was laid up in sheaves till we should have time to beat out the grain.

When we first moved from The Nest to the cave or Rock House, we could not find the handmill that we had brought from the ship. This now was found, and we took care to pack it up to take with us, as we would need it to grind our corn.

That night we slept once more in the great tree; but I must say that we did not sleep as soundly there as we used to do, nor did we feel so safe as we did in our rooms at Rock House.

The next day we were to start a plan in which our livestock would not need so much of our care. They had bred so quickly that we could spare some of them, and these I thought might be left in some place to seek their own food and yet be in reach should we need them.

My wife took from her hen roost ten young fowls, and I took four young pigs, four sheep, and two goats. These we put in our large cart, with such tools as we thought we would need, tied the black ox, the cow, and the donkey to the shafts,[16] and then set off from The Nest.

We had to cross a wide plain, and here we met with some dwarf plants on which, as Jack said, grew snowballs.

Fritz ran to see what they were and brought me a twig to which clung balls of snow white down. I held it up to show my wife, for I knew the sight would please her still more than it had her sons.

"See," I said, "this is the cotton plant, which you have often tried to find. It seems to grow here as thick as weeds, and, if I am a judge, it is of the best kind."

We got as much of this as our bags would hold, and my wife took care to pluck some of the ripe seed that we might raise a crop in our grounds at Tentholm.

At the end of the plain we came to the top of a high hill, from which the eye fell on

---

[16]shafts—*parallel poles that harness an animal to a vehicle*

a view like no other we had seen. Trees of all kinds grew on the sides of the hill, and a clear stream ran through the plain at its base and shone bright in the rays of the sun.

We said at once that this should be the site of our new farm. Close by we found a group of trees, the trunks of which, as they stood, would do for the main props of the house.

I had long had a mind to build a boat, and here I at last came on a tree that would suit. Fritz and I went for a mile or two in search of what we could find, and by the time we came back my wife had put up our tent for the night. We then all sat down to eat, and went to rest on beds made of the bags of cotton that we brought from the trees on the plain.

The next day we rose at dawn. The trees which were to form the frame of our farm-house stood on a piece of land eight yards long by five wide. I made a deep cut in each of the trunks, ten feet from the ground, and put up crossbeams to form a roof, on which we laid some bark in such a way that the rain would run off.

We were hard at work for some days at the Farm House. The walls we built of thin laths[17] and long reeds, woven tightly for six feet from the ground, but the rest we made of thin crossbars to let in both light and air. We made racks to store hay and other food for the livestock, and saved some grain for the fowls, for our plan was to come from time to time to feed them, till they got used to the place.

Our work took us more time than we thought; and as our store of food got low, we sent Fritz and Jack home to bring us a fresh stock and to feed the beasts we had left at Tentholm.

While they were gone, Ernest and I made a tour of the woods for some miles round the new farm. We first took the course of the stream that ran by the foot of the hill. Some way up we came to a marsh on the edge of a small lake, and here in the swamp grew a kind of wild rice, now ripe on the stalk, round which flew flocks of birds. I took some of the

---

[17]lath—*a strip of wood*

rice, that my wife might judge whether or not it was of use to us as food.

We went all the way around the lake, and saw plants and trees that were not known to me and birds that Ernest said he had not seen in any of the woods near The Nest. But we were most struck with the sight of a pair of black swans and a troop of young ones that came behind them. Ernest would have shot at them, but I told him not to kill what we did not need for food.

We did not get back till late in the day. Jack and Fritz, whom we met just as we came around the foot of the hill, had done their task well, for they had a good stock of food in a sack that lay on the back of the donkey, and they brought the good news that all was well at home.

We spent four more days at the farm, and then left it in such a state as to be fit for our use when we chose to go back to it.

The Farm House was but a part of our plan, for we had made up our minds to build a sort of stopping place, in which we could rest on our way to the farm. This took us six days to do. The spot we chose lay by the side of a brook, and was just such a place as would tempt one to stop and rest in the shade of the trees that grew on the bank. While at the brook, I made a boat out of the tree we found at the farm, and took it back with us to Tentholm in the cart.

We had still two months before the rain would set in, and this left us time to put the finishing touches on our cave. We laid the whole floor with clay and spread on it some fine sand, which we beat down till it was quite smooth and firm. On this we put sailcloth, and threw down goat's hair and wood made moist with gum. This was well beaten, and, when dry, made a kind of felt mat that was warm and soft to tread on and would keep the damp from our feet.

By the time these works were done, our cave was fit for us to dwell in. We did not now dread the rain, for we were safe out of its reach, and there was no need that we should go out in it. We had a warm shop to work in by day, a snug place where we could take our meals, and dry bedrooms in which we could sleep in peace.

Our livestock we kept in a shed at the back of the cave, and our storeroom held all that we could want.

When the rain at length set in, we all had some task that kept us busy in the cave. My wife worked at her spinning wheel or her loom, both of which I had made for her, for this kind of work appealed to her. With one of the wheels from the ship's guns I had made a lathe,[18] and with this I could turn legs for stools and chairs. Ernest, too, was fond of the lathe and soon learned to do such work quite as well as I.

At dusk, when we had done our work for the day, we brought out our stock of books and sat down to read by the light of a lamp.

At times, Jack and Franz would play a tune on their flutes, which I had made out of reeds; and my wife, who had a sweet voice, would sing some of the old Swiss songs that brought to our minds the joys of home.

Though we were by no means dull, nor in want of work to fill up our time, we were glad

---

[18]lathe—*a machine that rotates a piece of wood, allowing it to be shaped by a cutting tool*

when the time came for the rain to cease and we could gaze once more on the green fields. We went outside the first fine day and took a long walk by the base of the cliff. On the shore we found a dead whale, which the sea had no doubt thrown up in the storm. We had long felt the need of oil; for though we had a lamp, we had nothing but our wax lights to put in it, and these provided poor light to read by. The next day we cut up the whale and put the flesh in tubs. It was far from a clean job, for the oil ran down our clothes and made them smell; but as we could change them for new ones, we did not mind that, for the oil was now worth more to us than our clothes, though at one time we should not have thought so.

Chapter 9

Bears and Ostriches

One day late in the spring I went with my three sons a long way from Rock House. My wife and Franz were left at our stopping place to wait till we came back, but the dogs went with us. Our route lay far up the course of a small stream, which had its source some miles north of the Farm House. The ground was new to us, but we could not easily lose our way, for on the right stood a hill from which we could see the whole plain.

Ernest had gone with one of the dogs to a cave that he had spied at the foot of the hill, but we saw him turn around and run back with Turk at his heels. As soon as he thought his voice would reach us, he cried out, "A bear! A bear! Help me!"

We could now see that there were two great beasts at the mouth of the cave. At a word from us both the dogs flew to fight the bear that stood in front.

Fritz took up his post at my side, while Jack and Ernest kept in the rear. Our first shot was "a miss," as Jack said; but we took a sure aim the next time, and both shots met their mark. We would have shot at them once more from this spot, but as we thought we might hit our brave dogs, who were now in the heat of a hard fight with their foes, we ran up close to them.

"Now, Fritz," I said, "take a straight aim at the head of the first, while I fire on the one behind him."

We both shot at once; the bears gave a loud growl, and then with a moan, fell dead at our feet.

As it was now time to go back, we put the bears inside the cave.

We had a long walk back to the place where I had left my wife. The boys told her

what a hard fight the dogs had with the bears, and how Fritz and I had shot them. With the aid of Franz she had fed our livestock and brought in wood to make up our watch fire for the night, so we sat down to supper at once and then went to bed.

The next day we hitched our beasts to the cart and drove as far as the bears' den. It took us the whole day to cut up the bears. The hams were set aside to be smoke dried, while my wife took charge of the fat and the skins.

We now had so much work to do, and the days and weeks came and went so quickly, that I do not think we should have known the time of year had it not been for our log.

Some days were spent at Rock House, where we made our goods, ground our flour, stored our food, and kept our tame livestock. Then we had to take care of our crops on the fields near The Nest, and this took us two or three days in each month. Once every ten days we went to the farm on the hill, so that there was not a day that we didn't have our hands quite full. Now and then we went out to hunt for food or animals to add to our stock, which had grown so large that there were few we could name that had not been caught and brought home. We had birds of the air, fowls of the land, and beasts of all kinds, from the great black ox of the plain to the small wild rabbit that came and made its hole close by our cave.

But there was one bird that we had not yet caught, though we had seen it two or three times in the woods. This was the ostrich. Fritz found a nest with some eggs in it, and this led us to make a tour with the idea to catch one of the old birds. We rose that day before it was light and set out at dawn, each on the back of a good animal.

As we should have to hunt through the woods, my wife was left at home; and Ernest, who did not like rough work, chose to stay with her. We made it a rule to take one of the dogs with us when we went out to hunt, but on this day we thought it wise to let them both come.

Fritz took us straight to where he had seen the nest, which was not more than a few miles up the stream. When we came in sight of the spot, we saw four great birds, as if on their way to meet us. As they drew near we kept the dogs close to us, and made no noise, so that they did not stop till they came very near.

Fritz had brought his eagle with him, which he now let fly. At one swoop the bird came down on the head of the ostrich, held on with its beak, and struck out its wings with great force as if to stun the larger bird.

We now rode up close to the scene of the war. Jack first flung a cord around the legs of the bird. I then threw my pouch over its head, and, strange to say, it lay down as still as a lamb.

I now tied both its legs with cords, but left it just enough room to walk. We then tied it between the two bulls that had brought Jack and Franz all the way from home. The boys got up on the bulls, and I took the pouch from the head of the bird. As soon as it could see, it gave a wild stare and then fought to get free.

The boys then put spurs to the flanks of their animals, and when the bird had made a few starts back, as if to try the strength of the cords which held it, it set off with a run, and the bulls at each side made it keep up quite a pace.

Fritz and I now went in search of the nest, which we soon found. I took the eggs from it and put them in a bag I had brought to hold them, in which I put some wool and moss, so that they should not break.

It did not take us long to catch up to the two boys, who had gone on first, and we were glad to find that the poor bird had made up its mind to its fate and kept up well with the pace of the bulls.

When we got in sight of home, my wife and Ernest, who had been on the look out for us, came forth to meet us; and the strange way in which we brought home our new prize made them laugh. I need not say that we took great care of it.

The next day we built it a house with a space in front for it to walk up and down, around which were put rails so that it could not get out. At first it was shy and would not take any food, so that we had to force some balls of maize down its throat; but in a short time it took grain from the hands of my wife and soon grew quite tame.

The boys now set to work to break it in for use. They taught it first to carry them on its back. Then they put a pair of string reins in its mouth and had it turn which way they chose to pull, and walk, or run, or stand still, as it was bid. Thus, in a month from the time we caught it, the boys trained it to take them on its back to and from the farm or The Nest, in less than half the time an ox would go; so that it came to be the best animal we had to ride on.

The eggs we found in the nest were put in a warm dry place, and though we scarce thought our care would bring live birds out of the shells, we had the joy to hatch three of them, and this led us to hope that we should before long have a riding animal for each of our sons.

My work at this time was by no means light. Our hats and caps were all worn out, and with skins of the musk cat I had to make new ones. The bears' skins were laid in the

sun to dry, and of these we made fur coats, which would keep us warm when the cold, wet nights came, and there was some fur left to serve as rugs or quilts for our beds.

I now tried my hand at a new craft. I dug some clay out of the bed of the stream and taught the boys to knead it up with sand and some talc that had been finely ground. I had made a lathe with a wheel, and by its aid the clay left my hands in the shape of plates, cups, pots, and pans. We then burnt them in a rude kiln, and though at least one half broke with the heat and our want of skill, still those that came out whole more than paid me for my toil and kept up my wife's stock of dishes. Some of the jars were decorated with red and blue beads, and these were put on a shelf as works of art and kept full of long dried grass.

The time was now at hand when we must reap our grain and store the ripe crops that were still in the ground; and, in fact, there was so much to be done that we scarce knew what to do first. The truth must be told that our wants did not keep pace with the growth of our wealth; for the land was rich, and we had only a few mouths to fill.

We knew that we might leave the root vegetables in the ground for some time, as the soil was dry, but that the grain would soon spoil; so we made it our first care. When it was all cut and brought home, our next task was to thresh it. The floor of our storeroom was now as hard as a rock, for the sun had dried it, and there was not a crack to be seen. On this we laid the ears of ripe grain, from which the long straw had been cut. The boys were sent to bring in such of our livestock as were fit for the work to be done next.

Jack and Fritz were soon on the backs of oxen, and thought it fine fun to make them circle the floor and tread out the grain. Ernest and I had each a long fork, with which we threw the ears of grain at their feet, so that all of it might be trod upon. The ox on which Jack sat put down his head and took a bunch of the ears in his mouth.

"Come," said Jack, "it is not put there for you to eat, off you go!" and with that he gave it a lash with his whip.

"Stop!" I said, "do you not know what God has said in His Word?—We must not bind up the mouth of the ox that treads out the corn. In fact, the methods we are using to thresh our wheat is similar to those used by the Jews in the days of old."

To sort the chaff from the grain we threw it up with our spades while the breeze blew strong. The draft which came in at the door took the light chaff with it to one side of the room, while the grain fell straight to the ground by its own weight.

The maize we left to dry in the sun, and then beat out the grain with long skin thongs.[19] By this means we got a store of the soft leaves of this plant, which my wife made use of to stuff our beds.

When all the grain had been put in our storeroom, some in sacks and the rest in dry casks, we took a walk one day to our fields and found that flocks of birds, most of which were quails, had come there to feed. This provided us with plenty of fresh meat,

---

[19]thong—*a narrow strip, usually of leather*

and the next year we did not fail to look for them, so that the fields were made to yield a stock of game as well as a crop of grain.

With only slight changes in our lifestyle, we spent ten long years in our strange home. Yet the time did not seem long to us. Each day brought with it quite as much work as we could do, so that weeks and months and years flew past, till at last we gave up all hope that we should leave the island or see our old Swiss home, the thought of which was still dear to us.

But the lapse of ten years had wrought a great change in our sons. Franz, who was only a child when we first came, had grown up to be a strong youth; and Jack, at twenty, was as brave a lad as one could wish to see. Fritz, who was now a young man of twenty-five, took a large share of the work off of my hands. Ernest was two years younger, and his clever mind was as great a help to us as was the strength and skill of the rest.

It was a rare thing for the boys to be ill; and they were free from those sins which too often tempt young men to stray from

the right path. My wife and I did our best
to train them, so that they might know right
from wrong; and it gave us great joy to find
that what we told them sunk deep in their
hearts, and, like ripe seed sown in rich soil,
brought forth good fruit.

I need not say that in the course of ten
years we had made great strides in those arts
which our needs had first led us to learn.
When we first came, the land near Tentholm
was a bare waste; now it bore fine crops and
was kept as neat as a Swiss farm. At the
foot of the hill by the side of Rock House
was a large plot of ground, which we laid out
in beds, and here we grew herbs and shrubs,
and such plants as we used for food. Near
this we dug a pond, and by means of a chan-
nel which ran from the stream, we kept our
plants fresh in times of drought. Nor was this
the sole use we made of the pond; for in it we
kept small fish and crabs and took them out
with a rod and line when we had need of food
and time to spare for that kind of sport. In
the ground around the mouth of the cave we
drove a row of strong canes, bound at the top

to a piece of wood, so as to form a fence, up which grew a vine, and, at each side, plants that threw a good show of colorful blossoms crept up to meet it. Shells of great size and strange shapes were taken from the shore, and these we built up here and there with burnt clay, so as to form clumps of rock work, on which grew ferns and rare plants. All this gave a charm to our home, and made the grounds round it a source of joy when we finished our work for the day. In fact, we thought there was not anything to wish for that we did not have.

Our cares were few, and our life was as full of joy and peace as we could well wish; yet I often cast a look on the sea, in the hope that some day I should spy a sail and once more greet a friend from the wide world from which we had been so long shut out. This hope, vague as it was, led me to store up such things as would bring a price, if we had the chance to sell them; they might prove a source of wealth to us if a ship came that way, or would at least help to pay the charge of a cruise back to the land we came from.

It is only right to say that the boys did not share my hopes, nor did they seem to wish that we should leave the place where they had been brought up. It was their world, and Rock House was more dear to them than any other spot on earth.

"Go back?" Fritz would say; "to leave our cave, that we dug with our own hands; to part with our dear kind beasts and birds; to bid good-bye to our farms and so much that is our own. No, no! You cannot wish us to leave such a spot."

My dear wife and I both felt that age would soon creep on us, and we could not help having some doubts as to the future of our sons. Should we stay and end our days here, one of us would outlive the rest, and this thought brought with it a sense of dread I could not get rid of. It made me pray to God that He would save us all from so sad a fate as to die far from the sound of the voice of man, with no one to hear our last words, or lay us in the earth when He should call us to our rest.

My wife did not share this dread. "Why should we go back?" she would say. "We have here all that we can wish for. The boys lead a life of health, free from sin, and they live with us, which might not be the case if we were out in the world. Let us leave our future in the hands of God."

Chapter 10

Jenny

As Fritz and Ernest were now men, they were free to go where they chose and to come back when their will led them home. Thus, from time to time they took long trips and went far from Rock House. They had fine boats and strong animals, and of these they made such good use that there was scarcely a spot for miles around that was not well known to them.

At one time, Fritz had been so long from home that we feared he had lost his way or fallen prey to wild beasts. When he came back he told us a long tale of what he had seen and where he had been and how he had brought with him birds, beasts, moths, and such strange things as he thought Ernest would like to see. Later, he drew me out into our grounds and said he had a strange thing to tell me. It seems that he found a piece of white cloth tied to the foot of a bird, on which were these words: "Save a poor soul who is on the rock from which you may see the smoke rise."

He thought that this rock could not be far off, and that he ought to set off at once in search of it.

"I have a thought," he said; "I will tie a piece of cloth, like the one I found, to the leg of the bird, and on it I will write, 'Have faith in God; help is near.' If the bird goes back to the place from whence it came, our brief note may reach the eye of the lone one in the rock. At any rate, it can do no harm and may do some good."

He at once took the bird, which was an albatross, tied the strip of cloth to its foot, and let it go.

"And now," he said, "tell me what you think of this. If we should find a new friend, what a source of joy it will be. Will you join me in the search?"

"To be sure I will," I said; "and so shall the rest; but we will not yet tell them of this."

They were all glad to take a trip in the large boat, but they could not make out why we went in such haste.

"The fact is," said Jack, "Fritz has found some strange thing on the coast that he can't bring home, and he wants us to see it. But I dare say we shall know what it all means in good time."

Fritz was now our guide and went ahead of us in his bark canoe. In this he could go around the rocks of the coast, which would not have been safe for the large boat. He went up all the small creeks we met with on the way and kept a sharp eye out for the smoke by which he would know the rock we came out to find.

I must tell you that once when he came to these parts with Ernest he met with a tiger, and would have lost his life had it not been for his pet eagle. The brave bird, to save Fritz from the beast, made a swoop down on its head. Fritz thus got off with a scratch or two, but the poor bird was struck dead by a blow

from the paw of its foe. This was a sad loss
to Fritz, for his pet had been a kind friend and
would go with him at all times when he went
far from home.

There was scarcely a spot we came to
that did not bring to mind some such tale as
this, so that we were full of stories while the
boat bore us on.

We had been out several days, but could
find no trace of what we searched for. I rose
from my bed at dawn and went on deck with
Fritz. I told him that as we had no clue to
the place, we must now give up the search.
He did not seem to like this, but no more was
said. That day we spent on shore and came
back to our boat to sleep at night. Next day
we were to change our course and trace our
way back, for the wind now blew from the
sea.

When I went on deck next day I found
a short note from Fritz, in which he told me
that he could not give up the search, but had
gone some way up the coast in his small boat.
"Let me beg of you," he wrote, "to lie in wait
for me here till I come back."

When he had been gone two days, I felt that I ought to tell my wife the cause of our trip, as it might ease her mind. She heard me to the end and then said that she was sure he would not fail, but soon bring back good news.

As we were all looking for Fritz, we saw his boat a long way off.

"There is no one with him in the boat," I said to my wife; "that does not say much for our hopes."

"Oh, where have you been?" said the boys, all at once, as he came on board. But they scarce got a word from him. He then drew me to one side, and said, with a smile of joy, "What do you think is the news I bring?"

"Let me hear it," I said.

"I have found what I went forth to seek, and our search has not been in vain."

"And who is it that you have found?"

"Not a man," he said, "but a girl. The outfit she wears is that of a man, and she does not wish at first that her secret should be known, for she would not like to meet the family in those clothes, if they knew that she was a girl. And, strangest of all," said Fritz, "she has been on shore three years."

While I went to tell the news to my wife, Fritz had gone down to his room to change his clothes, and I must say that he took more care to look neat in his dress than usual.

He was not long, and when he came on deck he bid me say nothing to the rest about what he had found. He leaped like a frog into his canoe and led the way. We were soon on our course through the rocks and shoals,[20] and an hour's sail with the aid of a good breeze brought us to a small piece of land, the trees of which hid the soil from our view. Here we got close in to the shore and made our boat safe. We all got out and ran up the banks, led by the marks that Fritz had made in the soil with his feet. We soon found a path that led to a clump of trees, and there saw a hut, with a fire in front, from which rose a stream of smoke.

As we drew near I could see that the boys did not know what to make of it, for they gave me a stare, as if to ask what they were to see

---

[20]shoal—*a shallow place*

next. They did not know how to give vent to their joy when they saw Fritz come out of the hut with a strange youth whose slight build, fair face, and grace of form, did not seem to match well with the clothes that hung upon his limbs.

It was so long since we had seen a strange face, that we were all unwilling to speak first. When I could gain my speech I took our new friend by the hand and told her in words as kind as I could call to my aid, how glad we were to have thus found her.

Fritz, when he introduced Ernest and Jack, spoke of our new friend as Edward Montrose, but she could not hide her secret from my wife, for her first act was to fall on her shoulder and weep. The boys were quick to see through the trick and made Fritz tell them that "Edward" was not the name they should call her by.

I could not help noticing that our strange mode of life had made my sons rough and that years of rude toil had worn off that grace and ease which is one of the charms of the well-bred youth.

I saw that this made the girl shy of them and that the clothes she wore brought a blush to her cheek. I gave my wife charge of her, and she led the girl down to the boat, while the boys and I stood a while to speak of our fair guest.

When we got on board, we sat down to hear Fritz tell how he came to find Miss Jenny, for that was her real name; but he had not told half his tale when he saw my wife and her new friend come up on deck. Jenny, wearing a dress for which she had exchanged her sailor's suit, still had a shy look, but as soon as she saw Fritz she held out her hand to him with a smile, and this made us feel more at our ease.

The next day we were to go back to our home, and on the way Fritz was to tell us what he knew of Miss Jenny, for his tale had been cut short when she came on the deck with my wife. The boys did all they could to make her feel at home with them, and by the end of the day they were the best of friends.

The next day we set sail at sunrise; for we had far to go, and the boys had a strange wish to hear Fritz tell his tale.

When the boat had made a fair start, we all sat down on the deck, with Jenny in our midst, while Fritz told his tale to the end.

Jenny Montrose was born in India. She was the child of a British officer, Captain Montrose, whose wife died when Jenny was just a baby. When she was ten years of age her father sent her to a first class school, where she was taught all that was fit for the child of a rich man to know. In course of time she could ride a horse with some skill, and she then grew fond of most of the field sports of the East. As the Captain had to go from place to place with his troops, he thought that this kind of sport would train her for the life she would lead when she came to live with him. But this was not to be, for one day he told Jenny that he must leave the East and take the troops back to India. As it was a rule that no girl should sail on a ship with troops, he left her to the care of a friend who was to leave on another boat. He thought it best that she should dress like a young man while at sea, as there would then be no need for her to stay in her room. He knew that she was strong and brave and would like to go on deck to see the crew at their work. It gave the Captain pain to part with his child, but there was no help for it.

The ship had been several weeks at sea, when one day a storm broke over it, and the wind drove it for days out of its course. The crew did their best to steer clear of the rocks, but the ship struck a reef and sprung a leak. The boats then put off from the wreck, but a wave broke over the one in which Jenny rode, and she was borne, half dead with fright, to the place where we found her. She had been thrown high up on the beach and though faint and sick, got out of the reach of the waves. She did not know if those who were in the boat with her had lost their lives, but she had seen no trace of them since.

When she had strength to walk, she found some birds' eggs and shellfish, which she ate, and then went in search of some safe place where she could rest for the night. By good chance she had a flint and a knife; with these she set fire to some dry twigs, and this fire, she did not once let die out till the day we found her. Her life was at first hard to bear, but she was full of hope that someday a ship would come near the shore, to which she could make signs for help. The wild sports of the East in which she took part had made her limbs strong, and she had been taught to make light of such hardships that would weaken other girls.

She built a hut to sleep in and made snares to catch birds. Some of them she used for food, and some she let go with bits of cloth tied to their legs, on which she wrote words, in the hope that they might meet the eye of someone who could help her. This, as we know, had led Fritz to make his search, the end of which had brought as much joy to us as to the young friend who now sat in our midst.

When Fritz had told us this, and much more, we came in sight of Safety Bay. He then took Ernest with him in his small boat, to go up the stream as fast as they could to Rock House, so as to make the place look neat by the time we brought home our guest. The two boys—for to us they were still boys—met us on the beach. Fritz, with a look of pride, gave his hand to Jenny, and I could see a slight blush rise to her cheek as she gave him hers. He then led her up the path, on each side of which grew a row of young trees, and took her to a seat in our grounds. There he and Ernest had spread out a feast of our best food—fish, fowls, and fruit, and some of my wife's choice jam. We desired to show Jenny that, though the coast was a wild kind of place, still there were means to make life a joy to those who dwelt on it, if they chose to use them. As for Jenny, the sight of our home, the style of our feast, and the kind words of the boys were things so new to her that she knew not what to say.

"I shall tell no more than the truth," she said, "when I say that what you have shown me is of far more worth than all the wealth I have seen in the East, and that I feel more joy this day than I have felt in all the days of my life. I cannot use words less strong than these to show how much I thank you."

This was just the kind of speech to please the boys, for there had been no one to praise their work till now. When the meal was done, we made a tour of our house and grounds, that Jenny might see the whole place that from this time was to be her home. It would take me a long time to tell what she thought of all she saw, or the nice things she said in praise of our skill, as we took her from place to place. My wife's room, in which were kept the pots and pans to cook our food, and the plates, bowls, and cups, out of which we ate, took her some time to view; for she had long felt the lack of such things as she now saw we had made for our own use out of what we could find.

My wife found in Jenny a true friend, for the girl soon took a large share of the work off her hands and did it with so much skill and with so strong a wish to please us, that we grew to love her as if she had been our own child.

When the time came for us to keep indoors from the rain, the boys would often lay aside their work, and sit to hear Jenny talk of what she had seen in the East, and Ernest and Fritz would read to her from such books as she might choose. I was glad to see that this wrought a great change in my sons, whose mode of life had made them rough in their ways and loud in their speech—faults which we did not think of so long as there was no one to see or hear them.

When the spring came, the boys went in
our boat to the spot where they had found
Jenny and brought back some beans, which
were new to them. These we found to be
coffee. Jenny told us that they were by no
means scarce, but that she had not made use of
them, as she knew no way to roast or grind the
beans, which she found in a green state.

"Do you think," said my wife, "that the
plant would grow here?"

I then thought for the first time how fond
she was of it. There had been some bags on
board the ship, but I had not brought them
from the wreck; and my wife had once said that
she would like to see the plant in our ground.
Now that we knew where to get it, she told me
that it was one of the few things that she felt
the loss of. When the boys heard this, they
set out on a trip to bring back coffee plants,
and while there they went to the spot where
Jenny had dwelt for so long and sought for
what things she had left when she came to live
with us.

All these were brought to Rock House, and
I may tell you that Fritz set great store by them.

There were all sorts of odd clothes, which she had made of the skin of the sea calf; fishing lines made out of the hair of her head; pins made from the bones of fish; a lamp made out of a shell, with a wick of the threads which she had drawn from her leggings. There were the shells she used to cook her food in; a hat made from the breast of a large bird, the tail of which she had spread out so as to shade her neck from the sun; belts, shoes, and odd things of a similar kind.

My wife, who had now a friend to talk with, did not feel dull when the boys left us for a time, so they had permission to roam where their wish led them and to stay as long as they chose. In the course of time they knew the whole island on which we dwelt. Ernest drew a map of it to scale, so that we could trace their course from place to place with ease. When they went for a long trip they took some doves with them, and these birds brought us notes tied to their wings from time to time, so that we knew where they were and could point out the spot on the map.

I will not dwell on what took place now for some time, for I find that each year was very much like the last. We had our fields to sow, our crops to reap, our beasts to feed and train; and these cares kept our hands at work, and our minds free from the least thought of our lonely style of life.

I turn to my log as I write this, and on each page my eye falls on something that brings back to my mind the glad time we spent at Rock House.

Chapter 11

New Switzerland

In the spring of the year, when the rain was past, Fritz and Jack set off on a trip in their boat to Shark Isle. The day was fine, the sky clear, and there was no wind, yet the waves rose and fell as in a storm.

"Look!" cried Jack, "here comes a shoal[21] of whales. They will eat us up."

"There is no fear of that," said Fritz; "whales will do us no harm, if we do not touch them." This proved to be the case. Though any one of them might have broken up the boat with a stroke of its tail, they did not touch it, but swam by in a line, two by two, like a line of troops.

---

[21]shoal—*a large school of fish*

On Shark Isle, near the shore, we had built a fort, on which were set two of the ship's guns. These the boys made a rule to fire off to let us know that they were safe and to see if the guns were still fit for use. This time they found their charge quite dry, and the guns went off with a loud bang.

They had just put a plug in the hole of one of the guns to keep out the wet when they heard a sound roll through the air.

"Did you hear that?" said Jack. "I am sure that noise must have come from some ship at sea. Let us fire once more."

Then Fritz thought they ought to go home at once and tell me what they had heard. They both ran to the boat, and used all their strength to reach home before the sun went down.

The day was fine, and as the rain had kept us indoors for two months, we were glad to go down on the beach for a change. All at once I saw the boys come up the stream in their boat, at a great speed, and the way they used their oars led me to think that something was wrong.

"What have you seen that should thus put two brave youths to flight?" I said.

Then they told me what had brought them back so soon. I had heard the sound of the two guns which they had fired off, but no more. I told them I thought their ears must be at fault and that the sounds they had heard were no more than those of their own guns which the hills had sent back through the air. This view of the case did not at all please them, as by this time they well knew what sounds their guns made.

"It will be a strange thing," I said, "if the hope to which I have so long clung should at last come to be a fact; but we must be careful that we do not hail a crew which may rob and kill us for the sake of our wealth. I feel that we have as much cause to dread a foe as we have grounds of hope that we may meet with friends."

Our first course was to make the cave quite safe, and then to keep guard where we would see a ship if one should come near the coast. That night the rain came down in a flood, and a storm broke over us, and we were thus kept indoors for two days and two nights.

On the third day I set out with Jack to Shark Isle, to seek for the strange ship which he knew must be in some place not far from the coast. I went to the top of a high rock, but though my eye swept the sea for miles around, I could see no signs of a sail. I then made Jack fire three more shots, to see if they would give the same sound as the two boys had heard. You may judge how I felt, when I heard one! two! three! boom through the air.

There was now no room for doubt that, though I could not see it, there must be a ship near Shark Isle. Jack heard me say this and cried out with glee, "What can we do to find it?"

We had brought a flag with us, and I told Jack to haul this up twice to the top of the staff, which was a signal to those who saw it that we had good news to tell them.

I then left Jack on the fort with the guns and told him to fire as soon as a ship came in sight. I went back to Rock House to discuss with my wife, Jenny, and the boys, as to what steps we should now take. They all met me on the beach and made me tell them the news while I was still in the boat.

"We know no more," I said, "than the fact that there is still a ship on the coast. You must all now stay indoors, while Fritz and I go in search of it."

We set off at noon and went straight to the west part of the coast, where we thought the sound must have come from. We knew a cape there from which we could get a good view of the sea.

When we rounded the cape, great was our joy to find a fine ship in the bay. It was not far from us, for we could see the English flag float in the breeze from one of its masts. I seek in vain to find words that explain what I then felt. Both Fritz and I fell on our knees and gave thanks to God that He had thus led the ship to our coast. If I had not held him back, Fritz would have gone into the sea with a leap and swum off to the ship.

"Stay," I said, "till we are quite sure what they are. There are bad men on the seas who put up false flags to lure ships out of their course and then rob and kill the crew."

We could now see all that took place on board. Two tents had been set up on the shore, in front of which was a fire; and we could see that men went to and fro with planks. There were two men left on guard on the deck of the ship, and to these we made signs. When they saw us they spoke to someone who stood near, and whom we thought had charge of the ship. He then put his glass up to his eye and took a good view of us through it.

We both sang a Swiss song, and then I cried out at the top of my voice these words: "Ship ahoy! good men!" But they made no sign that they heard us. Our song, our boat, and, more than all, our dress, made them no doubt guess that we were wild men of the wood; for at last one of the crew on board held up knives and glass beads, which I knew the Indians of the New World were fond of. This made us laugh, but we would not as yet draw nigh to the ship, as we thought we ought to meet our new friends in our best clothes.

We then gave a shout and a wave of the hand and shot off around the cape as fast as our boat would take us. We soon got back to Rock House, where our dear ones were watching for us. My wife said we had done quite right to come back, but Jenny thought we should have found out who they were.

That night none of us slept well; Jenny thought there might now be a chance for her to reach her home, and she dreamed she heard the well-known voice of her father calling her to come to him. The boys were half crazed with vague hopes and lay for hours before they went to sleep. My wife and I sat up late to think and talk about the possibility of new opportunities. We felt that we were now full of years and should not like in our old age to leave the place where we had spent the best part of our lives; still we might do some trade with the land from which the ship came, if it were but known that we were here, and we might hear news of our dear Swiss home.

At daybreak we put on board our boat a stock of fruit and fresh food of all kinds, such as we thought the crew of the ship would like to have, and Fritz and I set sail for the bay. We took with us all the arms we could find, so as not to be at a loss should the crew turn out to be a set of thieves.

As we drew near the ship I fired a gun
and told Fritz to hoist a flag like theirs to the
top of our mast, and as we did so the crew
gave a loud cheer. I then went on board,
and the mate of the ship led me to his chief,
Captain Stone, who soon put me at my ease
by a frank shake of the hand. I then told
him who we were and how we came to dwell

on New Switzerland, as we had come to call our island. I learned from him, in turn, that he had sailed from Sydney, Australia; that he knew Captain Montrose, who had lost his child, and that he had made a search for her on the coast. He told me that a storm had thrown him off his course, and that the wind drove him on this coast, where he took care to fill his casks from a fresh stream that ran by the side of a hill and to take in a stock of wood.

"It was then," he said, "that we first heard your guns; and when on the third day the same sound came to our ears, we knew that there must be someone on the coast, and this led us to put up our tents and wait till the crew should search the land around the bay."

I then made the crew a gift of what we had brought in our boat and said to Captain Stone: "I hope, sir, that you will now go with me to Rock House, the place where we live, and there you will see Miss Montrose, who will be glad to hear some news of home."

"To be sure I will, and thank you much," he said; "and I have no doubt that Mr. Wolston

would like to go with us." This Mr. Wolston
was traveling with his wife and two girls
because a sea voyage had been recommended
to improve his health.

We all three then left the ship in our boat,
and as we came in sight of Shark Isle, Jack,
who was on the fort, fired his guns.

When we came to the beach, my wife and
the rest were there to meet us. Jenny was half
wild with joy when she heard that Captain
Stone had brought her good news from home.

We led them round our house and
through the grounds and Mr. Wolston took
note of all he saw. When we had a chance to
talk, I found that he had made up his mind to
stay with us in New Switzerland. I need not
say how glad I was to hear this, for he had
brought out with him a large stock of farm
tools, of which we had long been in want.

The boys were of course in high glee at all
this, but I did not share their joy so much as
I could wish. The ship which now lay close
to our shore was the first we had seen since
we came to the island, and no one could tell
when the next might come. My wife and I did

not wish to leave New Switzerland. I had a love for the kind of life we led, and we were both at an age when ease and rest should take the place of toil. But then our sons were young—not yet in the prime of life—and I did not think it right that we should keep them from the world. Jenny, I could tell, would not stay with us, nor did she hide from us the fact that her heart drew her to her father at home, from whom she had been kept so long. My wife and I told our boys to choose what they would do—to stay with us on the island, or leave with Captain Stone in the ship.

Ernest and Jack said they would not leave us. I saw that Fritz had made up his mind to go. I did not grieve at this, as I felt that our island did not give him the chance to learn all he could wish. I told him to speak out, and he said he should like to leave the place for a few years, and he knew Franz had a wish to go with him.

I thought this would give my wife pain, but she said that the boys had made a good choice, and that she knew Fritz and Franz would make their way in the world.

Captain Stone gave Jenny, Fritz, and Franz leave to go with him, as there was room in the ship now that the Wolstons were to stay with us.

The ship was brought around to Safety Bay, and Fritz and Jack went on board to fetch Mrs. Wolston and her two girls, who were glad to find that they were not to go back to the ship, for the storm had made them dread the sea.

I may here say, by the way, that Fritz and Jenny had grown fond of each other, and I felt that some day we should see them wed, which would be a fresh source of joy to us.

I have not much more to tell. The stores I had laid up—furs, pearls, spices, and fruits—were put on board the ship and left to the care of my sons, who were to sell them. And then the time came for us to part. I need not say that it was a hard trial for my wife; but she bore up well, for she had made up her mind that it was all for the best, and that her sons would one day come back to see her. I felt, too, that with the help of our new friends, we should not miss them so much as we at first thought, and this we found to be the case.

As my boys were to leave me the next day, I had a long talk with them. I told them to do their best in the new world in which they were to live, and to take as their guide the Word of God. They then knelt down for a prayer of blessing and went to their beds in Rock House for the last time.

I got no sleep all that night, nor did the two boys, who were to start the next day.

As Fritz takes this tale with him—which I gave him permission to print, that all may know how good God has been to us—I have no time to add more than a few words.

The ship that is to take from us our two sons and our fair guest will sail from this coast in a few hours, and by the close of the day, three who are dear to us will have gone from our midst. I cannot put down what I feel or tell the grief of my poor wife.

I add these lines while the boat waits for my sons. May God grant them health and strength for the trials they may have to pass through; may they gain the love of those with whom they are now to dwell; and may they uphold the good name of the Swiss Family Robinson.

❀ The End ❀